Focused Faith

Journal

Focused Faith
Journal

Intentionally Seeking God
& Counting My Blessings

TERESA RENEE HUNT

Focused Faith Journal:
Intentionally Seeking God & Counting My Blessings

Copyright © 2018, 2021 by Teresa Renee Hunt
Published by Truth2RenewHearts Publishing

For information: info@truth2renewheartspublishing.com

ALL RIGHTS RESERVED

No part of this publication may be reproduced, stored in a retrieval system, or transmitted in any form or by any means-electronic, mechanical, photocopying, recording, or otherwise without prior written permission of the publisher and copyright owners.

ISBN-13: 978-0986448218
ISBN-10: 0986448214

Cover design by Soleil Branding Essentials
Interior design by Madison Lux

Scripture quotations marked NIV are taken from The Holy Bible, New International Version® NIV® Copyright © 1973 1978 1984 2011 by Biblica, Inc. TM Used by permission. All rights reserved worldwide.

Scripture quotations marked ESV are taken from The Holy Bible, English Standard Version® (ESV®) Copyright © 2001 by Crossway, a publishing ministry of Good News Publishers. All rights reserved. ESV Text Edition: 2016

Scripture quotations marked KJV are taken from the Holy Bible, King James Version.

THIS JOURNAL BELONGS TO:
THIS YEAR:

Introduction

GOD IS....

Amazing, faithful, merciful, mighty, righteous, and holy. He is a provider, way maker, healer and protector. Our God is all-knowing and all-powerful. God is big and He is the great I AM.

By nature of *who* our God is, He manifests marvelous miracles in our lives every single day.

As we journey through our fast-paced life, we can very easily become preoccupied with *our* tasks, schedules, and reaching *our* goals, that we unintentionally take for granted the blessings and goodness of God in our lives. Other times, life's challenges and uncomfortable seasons may be so overwhelming that we overlook the provision and favor of God that is very present around us. Still, there are times when we may have all the intention in the world to remember every answered prayer, but because God is *always* moving, we are unable to recollect every single blessing by memory alone.

As believers, it's essential to remember that not only does God *do* good, but He *is* good. This means, because we have Jesus in our hearts, we can have joy and be grateful for, and in, every season of our lives. We are reminded in I Thessalonians 5:18 to give thanks in all circumstances, for giving thanks is God's will for us in Christ Jesus. Also, in the lyrics of Johnson Oatman Jr.'s timeless hymn, he encourages us to "*Count your blessings, name them one by one; Count many your blessings, see what God hath done*". With this journal, you can do just that: count your blessings as you recognize, recall, and give thanks for what God is doing within you, for you, and on your behalf.

My sister, God loves you passionately and unconditionally. As you think about the many ways God expresses His care for you, I pray you are inspired to draw deeper into His presence. As God's daughters created to bring Him glory through our lives, it is essential to our growth and spiritual development that we intentionally seek His face through worship, the Word, and spending time with Him in prayer. Being in His presence is refreshing, and Psalm 16:11 tells us that in His presence is the fullness of joy! What a blessing!

This *Focused Faith Journal* has been created for you to use as either a starting point for your dedicated time with God, or as a tool to complement your current devotional time. Oh yes, I know this journal is certainly larger than most. Its size was purposefully designed this way as a table-top journal where you can capsulate a year of blessings and gratitude in one place. There are 365 pages in this journal with space for you to count your blessings, write your prayers, relinquish your cares, and record great victories.

As you are deliberate about recognizing God's hand in your life, trusting Him wholeheartedly, and giving thanks in every circumstance, know that He has plans to prosper you, to give you a future, and hope as recorded in Jeremiah 29:11. Trust that He is working all things out for your good, and that He will do exceeding, abundantly, above all you can ask, think, or imagine, according to Romans 8:28 and Ephesians 3:20.

God is just *that* amazing!

HOW TO USE THIS JOURNAL

There are 4 sections on each page:

Wake. Pray. & Write

As you start your day early in the morning, carve out time to pray and write. Speak to God and listen as the Holy Spirit speaks to you. You can use this section to write a prayer, revelation of scripture, a vision, or to summarize what God is saying to you.

O God, thou art my God; early will I seek thee: my soul thirsteth for thee, my flesh longeth for thee.
PSALM 63:1A KJV

And the Lord answered me: "Write the vision; make it plain on tablets, so he may run who reads it.
HABAKKUK 2:2 ESV

Lord. I'm Casting These Cares Upon You

In this section of the journal, cast your cares upon the Lord. Remember, don't pray and worry. Write your cares and leave them there.

Casting all your care upon Him; for He careth for you.
1 PETER 5:7 KJV

Today's Wins & Accomplishments

Be on the lookout for the subtle and overt ways that God is making Himself evident around you, within you, and for you. Also, keep in mind that it is He who empowers you to achieve your goals each day. Before going to bed, be sure to record the triumphs that have taken place. This can be a personal accomplishment, a Kingdom win, or a victory of any kind. Nothing is too small or too big.

But thanks be to God! He gives us the victory through our Lord Jesus Christ.
1 Corinthians 15:57 KJV

And whatever you do, whether in word or deed, do it all in the name of the Lord Jesus, giving thanks to God the Father through him.
Colossians 3:17 NIV

Thank You, Lord!

This is the place where you can praise the Lord, express gratitude, and thank Him. Count your blessings so you can look back and see what God has done!

O give thanks unto the LORD, for He is good.
Psalm 107:1a KJV

Rejoice always, pray continually, give thanks in all circumstances; for this is God's will for you in Christ Jesus.
1 Thessalonians 5:16-18 NIV

THE FOCUSED FAITH CHALLENGE

It is my prayer that as you intentionally seek His face and count your blessings, your daily focus will increasingly be on God, and that you will be faithful in your relationship with Him just as He is to you. I **challenge** you to trust God daily and allow Him to guide you as you pursue His will for your life. Following His lead and His plan is the only way to truly prosper and live a powerful life. I also challenge you to wake, pray, and write in this journal every day. This journal is yours to infuse in your personal time with God. Reading the Bible each day is essential to your personal and spiritual growth. The more you spend time with Him the more you will know Him and recognize His faithfulness, grace, and presence in your life. May you experience great joy as you intentionally seek God and count your blessings with this *Focused Faith Journal.*

GET STARTED: READY, SET, GO!

I am thrilled that you have decided to make this journal a part of your faith journey. Before you dive in, take a moment to **share that you are a part of the Focused Faith Challenge** by posting a picture of yourself with this journal on social media, using the hashtag **#FocusedFaithChallenge.** Be sure to tag me @TeresaReneeHunt to let me know you have the journal! Your post will encourage others to join the challenge of walking by faith, trusting God, watching Him work, and focusing on Him. As you think about your enthusiasm and how this journal will greatly complement your walk with Christ, **please take a moment now to share a review on Amazon**. Your review on *Amazon.com* is greatly appreciated!

LET'S CONNECT

Lastly, lets connect! For encouragement, biblical inspiration, practical Bible teaching, and interactive livestream videos, follow me on social media and subscribe to my Youtube and Podcast channels.

Follow on Facebook: @TeresaReneeHunt
Follow on Instagram: @TeresaReneeHunt
Subscribe on Youtube: @TeresaReneeHunt
Subscribe to the Podcast: *www.teresareneehunt.com/podcast*

COMPLIMENTARY GIFT

Your words have the power to shape your world.

Change Your Words, Change Your Life: Powerful Declarations for the Purpose-Driven Woman is a **free *e-guide*** which includes ten Bible-based declarations and scriptures that will fortify your faith and empower you to walk boldly in your purpose.

Download your free copy: *www.teresareneehunt.com/declarations*

Cheers to all that God is doing and will continue to do in your life!

Yours in Christ,
Teresa Renee Hunt

TODAY'S DATE:

Wake, Pray, & Write

Lord, I'm Casting These Cares Upon You

Today's Wins + Accomplishments

Thank You, Lord!

TODAY'S DATE: ____________________

Wake. Pray. & Write

Lord. I'm Casting These Cares Upon You

Today's Wins + Accomplishments

Thank You. Lord!

TODAY'S DATE: ____________________

Wake. Pray. & Write

Lord, I'm Casting These Cares Upon You

Today's Wins + Accomplishments

Thank You, Lord!

TODAY'S DATE: ____________________

Wake. Pray. & Write

Lord. I'm Casting These Cares Upon You

Today's Wins + Accomplishments

Thank You. Lord!

TODAY'S DATE: ______________________

Wake. Pray. & Write

Lord, I'm Casting These Cares Upon You

Today's Wins + Accomplishments

Thank You, Lord!

TODAY'S DATE: ____________________

Wake. Pray. & Write

Lord, I'm Casting These Cares Upon You

Today's Wins + Accomplishments

Thank You, Lord!

TODAY'S DATE: ______________________

Wake. Pray. & Write

Lord. I'm Casting These Cares Upon You

Today's Wins + Accomplishments

Thank You. Lord!

TODAY'S DATE: ______________________

Wake, Pray, & Write

Lord, I'm Casting These Cares Upon You

Today's Wins + Accomplishments

Thank You, Lord!

TODAY'S DATE: ____________________

Wake. Pray. & Write

Lord, I'm Casting These Cares Upon You

Today's Wins + Accomplishments

Thank You, Lord!

TODAY'S DATE: ____________________

Wake, Pray, & Write

Lord, I'm Casting These Cares Upon You

Today's Wins + Accomplishments

Thank You, Lord!

TODAY'S DATE: ______________________

Wake, Pray, & Write

Lord, I'm Casting These Cares Upon You

Today's Wins + Accomplishments

Thank You, Lord!

TODAY'S DATE: ______________________

Wake. Pray. & Write

Lord. I'm Casting These Cares Upon You

Today's Wins + Accomplishments

Thank You. Lord!

TODAY'S DATE: ______________________

Wake, Pray, & Write

Lord, I'm Casting These Cares Upon You

Today's Wins + Accomplishments

Thank You, Lord!

TODAY'S DATE: ______________________

Wake. Pray. & Write

Lord, I'm Casting These Cares Upon You

Today's Wins + Accomplishments

Thank You, Lord!

TODAY'S DATE: ______________________

Wake. Pray. & Write

Lord, I'm Casting These Cares Upon You

Today's Wins + Accomplishments

Thank You, Lord!

TODAY'S DATE: ______________

Wake. Pray. & Write

Lord, I'm Casting These Cares Upon You

Today's Wins + Accomplishments

Thank You, Lord!

TODAY'S DATE: ______________________________

Wake. Pray. & Write

Lord, I'm Casting These Cares Upon You

Today's Wins + Accomplishments

Thank You, Lord!

TODAY'S DATE: ______________________

Wake, Pray, & Write

Lord, I'm Casting These Cares Upon You

Today's Wins + Accomplishments

Thank You, Lord!

TODAY'S DATE: ______________________

Wake. Pray. & Write

Lord, I'm Casting These Cares Upon You

Today's Wins + Accomplishments

Thank You, Lord!

TODAY'S DATE: ______________________

Wake. Pray. & Write

Lord. I'm Casting These Cares Upon You

Today's Wins + Accomplishments

Thank You. Lord!

TODAY'S DATE: ______________________

Wake. Pray. & Write

Lord. I'm Casting These Cares Upon You

Today's Wins + Accomplishments

Thank You. Lord!

TODAY'S DATE: ______________________

Wake, Pray, & Write

Lord, I'm Casting These Cares Upon You

Today's Wins + Accomplishments

Thank You, Lord!

TODAY'S DATE: ____________________

Wake, Pray, & Write

Lord, I'm Casting These Cares Upon You

Today's Wins + Accomplishments

Thank You, Lord!

TODAY'S DATE: ____________________

Wake. Pray. & Write

Lord. I'm Casting These Cares Upon You

Today's Wins + Accomplishments

Thank You. Lord!

TODAY'S DATE: ____________________

Wake. Pray. & Write

Lord, I'm Casting These Cares Upon You

Today's Wins + Accomplishments

Thank You, Lord!

TODAY'S DATE: ______________________

Wake, Pray, & Write

Lord, I'm Casting These Cares Upon You

Today's Wins + Accomplishments

Thank You, Lord!

TODAY'S DATE: ______________________

Wake. Pray. & Write

Lord, I'm Casting These Cares Upon You

Today's Wins + Accomplishments

Thank You, Lord!

TODAY'S DATE: ______________________

Wake. Pray. & Write

Lord. I'm Casting These Cares Upon You

Today's Wins + Accomplishments

Thank You. Lord!

TODAY'S DATE: ______________

Wake. Pray. & Write

Lord, I'm Casting These Cares Upon You

Today's Wins + Accomplishments

Thank You, Lord!

TODAY'S DATE: ______________________

Wake, Pray, & Write

Lord, I'm Casting These Cares Upon You

Today's Wins + Accomplishments

Thank You, Lord!

TODAY'S DATE: ______________________

Wake. Pray. & Write

Lord, I'm Casting These Cares Upon You

Today's Wins + Accomplishments

Thank You, Lord!

TODAY'S DATE: ______________________

Wake. Pray. & Write

Lord. I'm Casting These Cares Upon You

Today's Wins + Accomplishments

Thank You. Lord!

TODAY'S DATE: ____________________

Wake. Pray. & Write

Lord, I'm Casting These Cares Upon You

Today's Wins + Accomplishments

Thank You, Lord!

TODAY'S DATE: ______________________

Wake. Pray. & Write

Lord, I'm Casting These Cares Upon You

Today's Wins + Accomplishments

Thank You, Lord!

TODAY'S DATE: ______________________

Wake. Pray. & Write

Lord, I'm Casting These Cares Upon You

Today's Wins + Accomplishments

Thank You, Lord!

TODAY'S DATE: ______________________

Wake. Pray. & Write

Lord. I'm Casting These Cares Upon You

Today's Wins + Accomplishments

Thank You. Lord!

TODAY'S DATE: ______________________

Wake. Pray. & Write

Lord, I'm Casting These Cares Upon You

Today's Wins + Accomplishments

Thank You, Lord!

TODAY'S DATE: ______________________

Wake, Pray, & Write

Lord, I'm Casting These Cares Upon You

Today's Wins + Accomplishments

Thank You, Lord!

TODAY'S DATE:

Wake, Pray, & Write

Lord, I'm Casting These Cares Upon You

Today's Wins + Accomplishments

Thank You, Lord!

TODAY'S DATE: ______________________

Wake, Pray, & Write

Lord, I'm Casting These Cares Upon You

Today's Wins + Accomplishments

Thank You, Lord!

TODAY'S DATE: ____________________

Wake. Pray. & Write

Lord, I'm Casting These Cares Upon You

Today's Wins + Accomplishments

Thank You, Lord!

TODAY'S DATE: ______________________

Wake. Pray. & Write

Lord, I'm Casting These Cares Upon You

Today's Wins + Accomplishments

Thank You, Lord!

TODAY'S DATE: ______________________

Wake. Pray. & Write

Lord, I'm Casting These Cares Upon You

Today's Wins + Accomplishments

Thank You, Lord!

TODAY'S DATE: ______________________

Wake, Pray, & Write

Lord, I'm Casting These Cares Upon You

Today's Wins + Accomplishments

Thank You, Lord!

TODAY'S DATE: ______________________

Wake, Pray, & Write

Lord, I'm Casting These Cares Upon You

Today's Wins + Accomplishments

Thank You, Lord!

TODAY'S DATE: ______________________

Wake. Pray. & Write

Lord. I'm Casting These Cares Upon You

Today's Wins + Accomplishments

Thank You. Lord!

TODAY'S DATE:

Wake, Pray, & Write

Lord, I'm Casting These Cares Upon You

Today's Wins + Accomplishments

Thank You, Lord!

TODAY'S DATE: ____________________

Wake. Pray. & Write

Lord. I'm Casting These Cares Upon You

Today's Wins + Accomplishments

Thank You. Lord!

TODAY'S DATE: ____________________

Wake. Pray. & Write

Lord, I'm Casting These Cares Upon You

Today's Wins + Accomplishments

Thank You, Lord!

TODAY'S DATE: ______________________

Wake. Pray. & Write

Lord. I'm Casting These Cares Upon You

Today's Wins + Accomplishments

Thank You. Lord!

TODAY'S DATE: ______________________

Wake. Pray. & Write

Lord, I'm Casting These Cares Upon You

Today's Wins + Accomplishments

Thank You, Lord!

TODAY'S DATE: ______________________

Wake, Pray, & Write

Lord, I'm Casting These Cares Upon You

Today's Wins + Accomplishments

Thank You, Lord!

TODAY'S DATE: ____________________

Wake. Pray. & Write

Lord, I'm Casting These Cares Upon You

Today's Wins + Accomplishments

Thank You, Lord!

TODAY'S DATE: ______________________

Wake. Pray. & Write

Lord, I'm Casting These Cares Upon You

Today's Wins + Accomplishments

Thank You, Lord!

TODAY'S DATE: ______________________

Wake. Pray. & Write

Lord. I'm Casting These Cares Upon You

Today's Wins + Accomplishments

Thank You. Lord!

TODAY'S DATE: ______________________

Wake. Pray. & Write

Lord. I'm Casting These Cares Upon You

Today's Wins + Accomplishments

Thank You. Lord!

TODAY'S DATE: ______________________

Wake. Pray. & Write

Lord, I'm Casting These Cares Upon You

Today's Wins + Accomplishments

Thank You, Lord!

TODAY'S DATE: ______________________

Wake. Pray. & Write

Lord, I'm Casting These Cares Upon You

Today's Wins + Accomplishments

Thank You, Lord!

TODAY'S DATE: ____________________

Wake. Pray. & Write

Lord, I'm Casting These Cares Upon You

Today's Wins + Accomplishments

Thank You, Lord!

TODAY'S DATE: ____________________

Wake, Pray, & Write

Lord, I'm Casting These Cares Upon You

Today's Wins + Accomplishments

Thank You, Lord!

TODAY'S DATE: ______________________

Wake. Pray. & Write

Lord. I'm Casting These Cares Upon You

Today's Wins + Accomplishments

Thank You. Lord!

TODAY'S DATE: ____________________

Wake. Pray. & Write

Lord. I'm Casting These Cares Upon You

Today's Wins + Accomplishments

Thank You. Lord!

TODAY'S DATE: ____________

Wake. Pray. & Write

Lord, I'm Casting These Cares Upon You

Today's Wins + Accomplishments

Thank You, Lord!

TODAY'S DATE: ______________________

Wake. Pray. & Write

Lord, I'm Casting These Cares Upon You

Today's Wins + Accomplishments

Thank You, Lord!

TODAY'S DATE: ____________________

Wake. Pray. & Write

Lord, I'm Casting These Cares Upon You

Today's Wins + Accomplishments

Thank You, Lord!

TODAY'S DATE: ______________________

Wake. Pray. & Write

Lord, I'm Casting These Cares Upon You

Today's Wins + Accomplishments

Thank You, Lord!

TODAY'S DATE: ______________________

Wake. Pray. & Write

Lord, I'm Casting These Cares Upon You

Today's Wins + Accomplishments

Thank You, Lord!

TODAY'S DATE: ______________________

Wake. Pray. & Write

Lord. I'm Casting These Cares Upon You

Today's Wins + Accomplishments

Thank You. Lord!

TODAY'S DATE: ____________________

Wake. Pray. & Write

Lord, I'm Casting These Cares Upon You

Today's Wins + Accomplishments

Thank You, Lord!

TODAY'S DATE: ____________

Wake. Pray. & Write

Lord. I'm Casting These Cares Upon You

Today's Wins + Accomplishments

Thank You. Lord!

TODAY'S DATE: ______________________

Wake, Pray, & Write

Lord, I'm Casting These Cares Upon You

Today's Wins + Accomplishments

Thank You, Lord!

TODAY'S DATE: ______________________

Wake, Pray, & Write

Lord, I'm Casting These Cares Upon You

Today's Wins + Accomplishments

Thank You, Lord!

TODAY'S DATE: ____________________

Wake. Pray. & Write

Lord, I'm Casting These Cares Upon You

Today's Wins + Accomplishments

Thank You, Lord!

TODAY'S DATE: ______________________

Wake. Pray. & Write

Lord, I'm Casting These Cares Upon You

Today's Wins + Accomplishments

Thank You, Lord!

TODAY'S DATE: ______________________

Wake. Pray. & Write

Lord, I'm Casting These Cares Upon You

Today's Wins + Accomplishments

Thank You, Lord!

TODAY'S DATE: ______________________

Wake. Pray. & Write

Lord. I'm Casting These Cares Upon You

Today's Wins + Accomplishments

Thank You. Lord!

TODAY'S DATE: ______________________

Wake. Pray. & Write

Lord, I'm Casting These Cares Upon You

Today's Wins + Accomplishments

Thank You, Lord!

TODAY'S DATE: ____________________

Wake. Pray. & Write

Lord. I'm Casting These Cares Upon You

Today's Wins + Accomplishments

Thank You. Lord!

TODAY'S DATE: ______________________

Wake. Pray. & Write

Lord. I'm Casting These Cares Upon You

Today's Wins + Accomplishments

Thank You. Lord!

TODAY'S DATE:

Wake, Pray, & Write

Lord, I'm Casting These Cares Upon You

Today's Wins + Accomplishments

Thank You, Lord!

TODAY'S DATE: ____________________

Wake. Pray. & Write

Lord. I'm Casting These Cares Upon You

Today's Wins + Accomplishments

Thank You. Lord!

TODAY'S DATE: ______________________

Wake, Pray, & Write

Lord, I'm Casting These Cares Upon You

Today's Wins + Accomplishments

Thank You, Lord!

TODAY'S DATE: ____________________

Wake, Pray, & Write

Lord, I'm Casting These Cares Upon You

Today's Wins + Accomplishments

Thank You, Lord!

TODAY'S DATE: ____________________

Wake. Pray. & Write

Lord. I'm Casting These Cares Upon You

Today's Wins + Accomplishments

Thank You. Lord!

TODAY'S DATE: ______________________

Wake. Pray. & Write

Lord. I'm Casting These Cares Upon You

Today's Wins + Accomplishments

Thank You. Lord!

TODAY'S DATE: ______________________

Wake. Pray. & Write

Lord, I'm Casting These Cares Upon You

Today's Wins + Accomplishments

Thank You, Lord!

TODAY'S DATE: ______________________

Wake, Pray, & Write

Lord, I'm Casting These Cares Upon You

Today's Wins + Accomplishments

Thank You, Lord!

TODAY'S DATE: ______________________

Wake. Pray. & Write

Lord, I'm Casting These Cares Upon You

Today's Wins + Accomplishments

Thank You, Lord!

TODAY'S DATE:

Wake. Pray. & Write

Lord. I'm Casting These Cares Upon You

Today's Wins + Accomplishments

Thank You. Lord!

TODAY'S DATE: ______________________

Wake, Pray, & Write

Lord, I'm Casting These Cares Upon You

Today's Wins + Accomplishments

Thank You, Lord!

TODAY'S DATE:

Wake. Pray. & Write

Lord. I'm Casting These Cares Upon You

Today's Wins + Accomplishments

Thank You. Lord!

TODAY'S DATE: ______________________

Wake. Pray. & Write

Lord. I'm Casting These Cares Upon You

Today's Wins + Accomplishments

Thank You. Lord!

TODAY'S DATE: ______________________

Wake. Pray. & Write

Lord, I'm Casting These Cares Upon You

Today's Wins + Accomplishments

Thank You, Lord!

TODAY'S DATE: ____________________

Wake. Pray. & Write

Lord, I'm Casting These Cares Upon You

Today's Wins + Accomplishments

Thank You, Lord!

TODAY'S DATE: ______________________

Wake, Pray, & Write

Lord, I'm Casting These Cares Upon You

Today's Wins + Accomplishments

Thank You, Lord!

TODAY'S DATE: ______________________

Wake. Pray. & Write

Lord. I'm Casting These Cares Upon You

Today's Wins + Accomplishments

Thank You. Lord!

TODAY'S DATE: ______________________

Wake. Pray. & Write

Lord, I'm Casting These Cares Upon You

Today's Wins + Accomplishments

Thank You, Lord!

TODAY'S DATE:

Wake. Pray. & Write

Lord, I'm Casting These Cares Upon You

Today's Wins + Accomplishments

Thank You, Lord!

TODAY'S DATE: ______________________

Wake. Pray. & Write

Lord, I'm Casting These Cares Upon You

Today's Wins + Accomplishments

Thank You, Lord!

TODAY'S DATE: ______________________

Wake, Pray, & Write

Lord, I'm Casting These Cares Upon You

Today's Wins + Accomplishments

Thank You, Lord!

TODAY'S DATE: ______________________

Wake. Pray. & Write

Lord. I'm Casting These Cares Upon You

Today's Wins + Accomplishments

Thank You. Lord!

TODAY'S DATE: ______________________________

Wake. Pray. & Write

Lord. I'm Casting These Cares Upon You

Today's Wins + Accomplishments

Thank You. Lord!

TODAY'S DATE: ______________________

Wake, Pray, & Write

Lord, I'm Casting These Cares Upon You

Today's Wins + Accomplishments

Thank You, Lord!

TODAY'S DATE: ____________________

Wake. Pray. & Write

Lord. I'm Casting These Cares Upon You

Today's Wins + Accomplishments

Thank You. Lord!

TODAY'S DATE: ________________

Wake. Pray. & Write

Lord. I'm Casting These Cares Upon You

Today's Wins + Accomplishments

Thank You. Lord!

TODAY'S DATE: ______________________

Wake. Pray. & Write

Lord, I'm Casting These Cares Upon You

Today's Wins + Accomplishments

Thank You, Lord!

TODAY'S DATE: ____________________

Wake. Pray. & Write

Lord, I'm Casting These Cares Upon You

Today's Wins + Accomplishments

Thank You, Lord!

TODAY'S DATE:

Wake. Pray. & Write

Lord. I'm Casting These Cares Upon You

Today's Wins + Accomplishments

Thank You. Lord!

TODAY'S DATE: ______________________

Wake, Pray, & Write

Lord, I'm Casting These Cares Upon You

Today's Wins + Accomplishments

Thank You, Lord!

TODAY'S DATE: ______________________________

Wake, Pray, & Write

Lord, I'm Casting These Cares Upon You

Today's Wins + Accomplishments

Thank You, Lord!

TODAY'S DATE: ____________________

Wake, Pray, & Write

Lord, I'm Casting These Cares Upon You

Today's Wins + Accomplishments

Thank You, Lord!

TODAY'S DATE: ______________________

Wake, Pray, & Write

Lord, I'm Casting These Cares Upon You

Today's Wins + Accomplishments

Thank You, Lord!

TODAY'S DATE: ____________________

Wake. Pray. & Write

Lord, I'm Casting These Cares Upon You

Today's Wins + Accomplishments

Thank You, Lord!

TODAY'S DATE: ____________________

Wake, Pray, & Write

Lord, I'm Casting These Cares Upon You

Today's Wins + Accomplishments

Thank You, Lord!

TODAY'S DATE: ______________________

Wake. Pray. & Write

Lord, I'm Casting These Cares Upon You

Today's Wins + Accomplishments

Thank You, Lord!

TODAY'S DATE: ______________

Wake. Pray. & Write

Lord. I'm Casting These Cares Upon You

Today's Wins + Accomplishments

Thank You. Lord!

TODAY'S DATE: ____________________

Wake. Pray. & Write

Lord. I'm Casting These Cares Upon You

Today's Wins + Accomplishments

Thank You. Lord!

TODAY'S DATE: ______________________

Wake. Pray. & Write

Lord. I'm Casting These Cares Upon You

Today's Wins + Accomplishments

Thank You. Lord!

TODAY'S DATE: ______________________

Wake. Pray. & Write

Lord, I'm Casting These Cares Upon You

Today's Wins + Accomplishments

Thank You, Lord!

TODAY'S DATE: ______________________

Wake. Pray. & Write

Lord, I'm Casting These Cares Upon You

Today's Wins + Accomplishments

Thank You, Lord!

TODAY'S DATE: ______________________________

Wake, Pray, & Write

Lord, I'm Casting These Cares Upon You

Today's Wins + Accomplishments

Thank You, Lord!

TODAY'S DATE: ______________________

Wake, Pray, & Write

Lord, I'm Casting These Cares Upon You

Today's Wins + Accomplishments

Thank You, Lord!

TODAY'S DATE: ______________________

Wake. Pray. & Write

Lord. I'm Casting These Cares Upon You

Today's Wins + Accomplishments

Thank You. Lord!

TODAY'S DATE: ______________________

Wake, Pray, & Write

Lord, I'm Casting These Cares Upon You

Today's Wins + Accomplishments

Thank You, Lord!

TODAY'S DATE: ______________________

Wake, Pray, & Write

Lord, I'm Casting These Cares Upon You

Today's Wins + Accomplishments

Thank You, Lord!

TODAY'S DATE: ______________________

Wake. Pray. & Write

Lord. I'm Casting These Cares Upon You

Today's Wins + Accomplishments

Thank You. Lord!

TODAY'S DATE: ____________________

Wake. Pray. & Write

Lord, I'm Casting These Cares Upon You

Today's Wins + Accomplishments

Thank You, Lord!

TODAY'S DATE: ______________________

Wake. Pray. & Write

Lord. I'm Casting These Cares Upon You

Today's Wins + Accomplishments

Thank You. Lord!

TODAY'S DATE: ______________________

Wake. Pray. & Write

Lord. I'm Casting These Cares Upon You

Today's Wins + Accomplishments

Thank You. Lord!

TODAY'S DATE: ______________________

Wake. Pray. & Write

Lord, I'm Casting These Cares Upon You

Today's Wins + Accomplishments

Thank You, Lord!

TODAY'S DATE: ______________________

Wake, Pray, & Write

Lord, I'm Casting These Cares Upon You

Today's Wins + Accomplishments

Thank You, Lord!

TODAY'S DATE: ______________________

Wake. Pray. & Write

Lord. I'm Casting These Cares Upon You

Today's Wins + Accomplishments

Thank You. Lord!

TODAY'S DATE: ____________________

Wake. Pray. & Write

Lord, I'm Casting These Cares Upon You

Today's Wins + Accomplishments

Thank You, Lord!

TODAY'S DATE: ______________________

Wake. Pray. & Write

Lord, I'm Casting These Cares Upon You

Today's Wins + Accomplishments

Thank You, Lord!

TODAY'S DATE: ______________________

Wake, Pray, & Write

Lord, I'm Casting These Cares Upon You

Today's Wins + Accomplishments

Thank You, Lord!

TODAY'S DATE: ______________________

Wake. Pray. & Write

Lord. I'm Casting These Cares Upon You

Today's Wins + Accomplishments

Thank You. Lord!

TODAY'S DATE: ____________________

Wake. Pray. & Write

Lord, I'm Casting These Cares Upon You

Today's Wins + Accomplishments

Thank You, Lord!

TODAY'S DATE: ____________

Wake. Pray. & Write

Lord. I'm Casting These Cares Upon You

Today's Wins + Accomplishments

Thank You. Lord!

TODAY'S DATE: ____________________

Wake. Pray. & Write

Lord. I'm Casting These Cares Upon You

Today's Wins + Accomplishments

Thank You. Lord!

TODAY'S DATE:

Wake. Pray. & Write

Lord. I'm Casting These Cares Upon You

Today's Wins + Accomplishments

Thank You. Lord!

TODAY'S DATE: ______________________

Wake. Pray. & Write

Lord, I'm Casting These Cares Upon You

Today's Wins + Accomplishments

Thank You, Lord!

TODAY'S DATE: ____________________

Wake. Pray. & Write

Lord, I'm Casting These Cares Upon You

Today's Wins + Accomplishments

Thank You, Lord!

TODAY'S DATE:

Wake. Pray. & Write

Lord, I'm Casting These Cares Upon You

Today's Wins + Accomplishments

Thank You, Lord!

TODAY'S DATE: ___________________________

Wake, Pray, & Write

Lord, I'm Casting These Cares Upon You

Today's Wins + Accomplishments

Thank You, Lord!

TODAY'S DATE: ______________________

Wake. Pray. & Write

Lord, I'm Casting These Cares Upon You

Today's Wins + Accomplishments

Thank You, Lord!

TODAY'S DATE: ______________________

Wake. Pray. & Write

Lord. I'm Casting These Cares Upon You

Today's Wins + Accomplishments

Thank You. Lord!

TODAY'S DATE: ______________________

Wake. Pray. & Write

Lord, I'm Casting These Cares Upon You

Today's Wins + Accomplishments

Thank You, Lord!

TODAY'S DATE: ______________________

Wake. Pray. & Write

Lord. I'm Casting These Cares Upon You

Today's Wins + Accomplishments

Thank You. Lord!

TODAY'S DATE: ______________________

Wake. Pray. & Write

Lord, I'm Casting These Cares Upon You

Today's Wins + Accomplishments

Thank You, Lord!

TODAY'S DATE: ____________________

Wake, Pray, & Write

Lord, I'm Casting These Cares Upon You

Today's Wins + Accomplishments

Thank You, Lord!

TODAY'S DATE:

Wake, Pray, & Write

Lord, I'm Casting These Cares Upon You

Today's Wins + Accomplishments

Thank You, Lord!

TODAY'S DATE: ______________________

Wake, Pray, & Write

Lord, I'm Casting These Cares Upon You

Today's Wins + Accomplishments

Thank You, Lord!

TODAY'S DATE: ____________________

Wake. Pray. & Write

Lord. I'm Casting These Cares Upon You

Today's Wins + Accomplishments

Thank You. Lord!

TODAY'S DATE: ______________________

Wake. Pray. & Write

Lord, I'm Casting These Cares Upon You

Today's Wins + Accomplishments

Thank You, Lord!

TODAY'S DATE: ______________________

Wake, Pray, & Write

Lord, I'm Casting These Cares Upon You

Today's Wins + Accomplishments

Thank You, Lord!

TODAY'S DATE: ______________________

Wake, Pray, & Write

Lord, I'm Casting These Cares Upon You

Today's Wins + Accomplishments

Thank You, Lord!

TODAY'S DATE:

Wake, Pray, & Write

Lord, I'm Casting These Cares Upon You

Today's Wins + Accomplishments

Thank You, Lord!

TODAY'S DATE: ______________________

Wake, Pray, & Write

Lord, I'm Casting These Cares Upon You

Today's Wins + Accomplishments

Thank You, Lord!

TODAY'S DATE: ______________________________

Wake. Pray. & Write

Lord, I'm Casting These Cares Upon You

Today's Wins + Accomplishments

Thank You, Lord!

TODAY'S DATE: ______________________

Wake. Pray. & Write

Lord. I'm Casting These Cares Upon You

Today's Wins + Accomplishments

Thank You. Lord!

TODAY'S DATE: ______________________

Wake. Pray. & Write

Lord. I'm Casting These Cares Upon You

Today's Wins + Accomplishments

Thank You. Lord!

TODAY'S DATE: ______________________

Wake. Pray. & Write

Lord. I'm Casting These Cares Upon You

Today's Wins + Accomplishments

Thank You. Lord!

TODAY'S DATE: ____________________

Wake, Pray, & Write

Lord, I'm Casting These Cares Upon You

Today's Wins + Accomplishments

Thank You, Lord!

TODAY'S DATE: ______________________

Wake. Pray. & Write

Lord. I'm Casting These Cares Upon You

Today's Wins + Accomplishments

Thank You. Lord!

TODAY'S DATE: ____________________

Wake. Pray. & Write

Lord. I'm Casting These Cares Upon You

Today's Wins + Accomplishments

Thank You. Lord!

TODAY'S DATE: ______

Wake, Pray, & Write

Lord, I'm Casting These Cares Upon You

Today's Wins + Accomplishments

Thank You, Lord!

TODAY'S DATE: ______________________

Wake. Pray. & Write

Lord, I'm Casting These Cares Upon You

Today's Wins + Accomplishments

Thank You, Lord!

TODAY'S DATE: ______________________

Wake, Pray, & Write

Lord, I'm Casting These Cares Upon You

Today's Wins + Accomplishments

Thank You, Lord!

TODAY'S DATE: ____________________

Wake. Pray. & Write

Lord, I'm Casting These Cares Upon You

Today's Wins + Accomplishments

Thank You, Lord!

TODAY'S DATE: ____________________

Wake, Pray, & Write

Lord, I'm Casting These Cares Upon You

Today's Wins + Accomplishments

Thank You, Lord!

TODAY'S DATE: ______________________

Wake, Pray, & Write

Lord, I'm Casting These Cares Upon You

Today's Wins + Accomplishments

Thank You, Lord!

TODAY'S DATE: ______________________

Wake. Pray. & Write

Lord. I'm Casting These Cares Upon You

Today's Wins + Accomplishments

Thank You. Lord!

TODAY'S DATE:

Wake, Pray, & Write

Lord, I'm Casting These Cares Upon You

Today's Wins + Accomplishments

Thank You, Lord!

TODAY'S DATE: ______________________

Wake, Pray, & Write

Lord, I'm Casting These Cares Upon You

Today's Wins + Accomplishments

Thank You, Lord!

TODAY'S DATE: ______________________

Wake, Pray, & Write

Lord, I'm Casting These Cares Upon You

Today's Wins + Accomplishments

Thank You, Lord!

TODAY'S DATE: ______________________

Wake, Pray, & Write

Lord, I'm Casting These Cares Upon You

Today's Wins + Accomplishments

Thank You, Lord!

TODAY'S DATE:

Wake. Pray. & Write

Lord. I'm Casting These Cares Upon You

Today's Wins + Accomplishments

Thank You. Lord!

TODAY'S DATE: ______________________

Wake. Pray. & Write

Lord. I'm Casting These Cares Upon You

Today's Wins + Accomplishments

Thank You. Lord!

TODAY'S DATE: ______________________

Wake. Pray. & Write

Lord, I'm Casting These Cares Upon You

Today's Wins + Accomplishments

Thank You, Lord!

TODAY'S DATE: ____________________

Wake. Pray. & Write

Lord. I'm Casting These Cares Upon You

Today's Wins + Accomplishments

Thank You. Lord!

TODAY'S DATE: ______________________

Wake, Pray, & Write

Lord, I'm Casting These Cares Upon You

Today's Wins + Accomplishments

Thank You, Lord!

TODAY'S DATE: ______________________

Wake, Pray, & Write

Lord, I'm Casting These Cares Upon You

Today's Wins + Accomplishments

Thank You, Lord!

TODAY'S DATE: ______________________________

Wake. Pray. & Write

Lord, I'm Casting These Cares Upon You

Today's Wins + Accomplishments

Thank You, Lord!

TODAY'S DATE: ______________________

Wake. Pray. & Write

Lord. I'm Casting These Cares Upon You

Today's Wins + Accomplishments

Thank You. Lord!

TODAY'S DATE: ______________________

Wake, Pray, & Write

Lord, I'm Casting These Cares Upon You

Today's Wins + Accomplishments

Thank You, Lord!

TODAY'S DATE: ____________________

Wake. Pray. & Write

Lord. I'm Casting These Cares Upon You

Today's Wins + Accomplishments

Thank You. Lord!

TODAY'S DATE: ______________________

Wake, Pray, & Write

Lord, I'm Casting These Cares Upon You

Today's Wins + Accomplishments

Thank You, Lord!

TODAY'S DATE: ______________________

Wake. Pray. & Write

Lord. I'm Casting These Cares Upon You

Today's Wins + Accomplishments

Thank You. Lord!

TODAY'S DATE:

Wake, Pray, & Write

Lord, I'm Casting These Cares Upon You

Today's Wins + Accomplishments

Thank You, Lord!

TODAY'S DATE: ______________________

Wake. Pray. & Write

Lord. I'm Casting These Cares Upon You

Today's Wins + Accomplishments

Thank You. Lord!

TODAY'S DATE: ____________________

Wake. Pray. & Write

Lord, I'm Casting These Cares Upon You

Today's Wins + Accomplishments

Thank You, Lord!

TODAY'S DATE: ______________________

Wake. Pray. & Write

Lord. I'm Casting These Cares Upon You

Today's Wins + Accomplishments

Thank You. Lord!

TODAY'S DATE: ______________________

Wake. Pray. & Write

Lord, I'm Casting These Cares Upon You

Today's Wins + Accomplishments

Thank You, Lord!

TODAY'S DATE: ______________________

Wake. Pray. & Write

Lord. I'm Casting These Cares Upon You

Today's Wins + Accomplishments

Thank You. Lord!

TODAY'S DATE: ____________

Wake. Pray. & Write

Lord, I'm Casting These Cares Upon You

Today's Wins + Accomplishments

Thank You, Lord!

TODAY'S DATE: ______________________

Wake, Pray, & Write

Lord, I'm Casting These Cares Upon You

Today's Wins + Accomplishments

Thank You, Lord!

TODAY'S DATE: ____________________

Wake. Pray. & Write

Lord. I'm Casting These Cares Upon You

Today's Wins + Accomplishments

Thank You. Lord!

TODAY'S DATE: ______________________

Wake, Pray, & Write

Lord, I'm Casting These Cares Upon You

Today's Wins + Accomplishments

Thank You, Lord!

TODAY'S DATE: ___

Wake. Pray. & Write

Lord. I'm Casting These Cares Upon You

Today's Wins + Accomplishments

Thank You. Lord!

TODAY'S DATE: ______________________

Wake. Pray. & Write

Lord. I'm Casting These Cares Upon You

Today's Wins + Accomplishments

Thank You. Lord!

TODAY'S DATE: ______________________

Wake. Pray. & Write

Lord, I'm Casting These Cares Upon You

Today's Wins + Accomplishments

Thank You, Lord!

TODAY'S DATE: ______________________

Wake, Pray, & Write

Lord, I'm Casting These Cares Upon You

Today's Wins + Accomplishments

Thank You, Lord!

TODAY'S DATE: ____________________

Wake, Pray, & Write

Lord, I'm Casting These Cares Upon You

Today's Wins + Accomplishments

Thank You, Lord!

TODAY'S DATE: ____________________

Wake. Pray. & Write

Lord. I'm Casting These Cares Upon You

Today's Wins + Accomplishments

Thank You. Lord!

TODAY'S DATE: ______________________

Wake. Pray. & Write

Lord, I'm Casting These Cares Upon You

Today's Wins + Accomplishments

Thank You, Lord!

TODAY'S DATE: ______________________

Wake. Pray. & Write

Lord, I'm Casting These Cares Upon You

Today's Wins + Accomplishments

Thank You, Lord!

TODAY'S DATE: ____________________

Wake. Pray. & Write

Lord, I'm Casting These Cares Upon You

Today's Wins + Accomplishments

Thank You, Lord!

TODAY'S DATE: ____________________

Wake. Pray. & Write

Lord. I'm Casting These Cares Upon You

Today's Wins + Accomplishments

Thank You. Lord!

TODAY'S DATE: ______________________

Wake, Pray, & Write

Lord, I'm Casting These Cares Upon You

Today's Wins + Accomplishments

Thank You, Lord!

TODAY'S DATE: ______________________

Wake. Pray. & Write

Lord, I'm Casting These Cares Upon You

Today's Wins + Accomplishments

Thank You, Lord!

TODAY'S DATE: ______________________

Wake, Pray, & Write

Lord, I'm Casting These Cares Upon You

Today's Wins + Accomplishments

Thank You, Lord!

TODAY'S DATE: ____________________

Wake, Pray, & Write

Lord, I'm Casting These Cares Upon You

Today's Wins + Accomplishments

Thank You, Lord!

TODAY'S DATE: ______________________

Wake, Pray, & Write

Lord, I'm Casting These Cares Upon You

Today's Wins + Accomplishments

Thank You, Lord!

TODAY'S DATE: ______________________

Wake. Pray. & Write

Lord, I'm Casting These Cares Upon You

Today's Wins + Accomplishments

Thank You, Lord!

TODAY'S DATE: ______________________

Wake, Pray, & Write

Lord, I'm Casting These Cares Upon You

Today's Wins + Accomplishments

Thank You, Lord!

TODAY'S DATE: ______________________

Wake. Pray. & Write

Lord. I'm Casting These Cares Upon You

Today's Wins + Accomplishments

Thank You. Lord!

TODAY'S DATE: ______________________

Wake. Pray. & Write

Lord. I'm Casting These Cares Upon You

Today's Wins + Accomplishments

Thank You. Lord!

TODAY'S DATE: ____________________

Wake, Pray, & Write

Lord, I'm Casting These Cares Upon You

Today's Wins + Accomplishments

Thank You, Lord!

TODAY'S DATE: ____________________

Wake. Pray. & Write

Lord. I'm Casting These Cares Upon You

Today's Wins + Accomplishments

Thank You. Lord!

TODAY'S DATE: ______________________

Wake. Pray. & Write

Lord. I'm Casting These Cares Upon You

Today's Wins + Accomplishments

Thank You. Lord!

TODAY'S DATE: ______________________

Wake, Pray, & Write

Lord, I'm Casting These Cares Upon You

Today's Wins + Accomplishments

Thank You, Lord!

TODAY'S DATE: ______________________

Wake. Pray. & Write

Lord. I'm Casting These Cares Upon You

Today's Wins + Accomplishments

Thank You. Lord!

TODAY'S DATE: ____________________

Wake. Pray. & Write

Lord, I'm Casting These Cares Upon You

Today's Wins + Accomplishments

Thank You, Lord!

TODAY'S DATE: ____________________

Wake, Pray, & Write

Lord, I'm Casting These Cares Upon You

Today's Wins + Accomplishments

Thank You, Lord!

TODAY'S DATE: ______________________

Wake. Pray. & Write

Lord, I'm Casting These Cares Upon You

Today's Wins + Accomplishments

Thank You, Lord!

TODAY'S DATE: ______________________________

Wake. Pray. & Write

Lord. I'm Casting These Cares Upon You

Today's Wins + Accomplishments

Thank You. Lord!

TODAY'S DATE: ______________________

Wake, Pray, & Write

Lord, I'm Casting These Cares Upon You

Today's Wins + Accomplishments

Thank You, Lord!

TODAY'S DATE: ____________________

Wake. Pray. & Write

Lord, I'm Casting These Cares Upon You

Today's Wins + Accomplishments

Thank You, Lord!

TODAY'S DATE: ______________________

Wake. Pray. & Write

Lord. I'm Casting These Cares Upon You

Today's Wins + Accomplishments

Thank You. Lord!

TODAY'S DATE: ______________________

Wake. Pray. & Write

Lord. I'm Casting These Cares Upon You

Today's Wins + Accomplishments

Thank You. Lord!

TODAY'S DATE: ____________________

Wake. Pray. & Write

Lord, I'm Casting These Cares Upon You

Today's Wins + Accomplishments

Thank You, Lord!

TODAY'S DATE: ______________________

Wake, Pray, & Write

Lord, I'm Casting These Cares Upon You

Today's Wins + Accomplishments

Thank You, Lord!

TODAY'S DATE: ____________________

Wake. Pray. & Write

Lord, I'm Casting These Cares Upon You

Today's Wins + Accomplishments

Thank You, Lord!

TODAY'S DATE:

Wake. Pray. & Write

Lord. I'm Casting These Cares Upon You

Today's Wins + Accomplishments

Thank You. Lord!

TODAY'S DATE: ____________________

Wake, Pray, & Write

Lord, I'm Casting These Cares Upon You

Today's Wins + Accomplishments

Thank You, Lord!

TODAY'S DATE: ______________________

Wake. Pray. & Write

Lord. I'm Casting These Cares Upon You

Today's Wins + Accomplishments

Thank You. Lord!

TODAY'S DATE: ______________________

Wake. Pray. & Write

Lord. I'm Casting These Cares Upon You

Today's Wins + Accomplishments

Thank You. Lord!

TODAY'S DATE: ______________________

Wake. Pray. & Write

Lord, I'm Casting These Cares Upon You

Today's Wins + Accomplishments

Thank You, Lord!

TODAY'S DATE: ____________________

Wake. Pray. & Write

Lord, I'm Casting These Cares Upon You

Today's Wins + Accomplishments

Thank You, Lord!

TODAY'S DATE: ____________________

Wake. Pray. & Write

Lord. I'm Casting These Cares Upon You

Today's Wins + Accomplishments

Thank You. Lord!

TODAY'S DATE: ______________________

Wake. Pray. & Write

Lord, I'm Casting These Cares Upon You

Today's Wins + Accomplishments

Thank You, Lord!

TODAY'S DATE: ____________________

Wake. Pray. & Write

Lord. I'm Casting These Cares Upon You

Today's Wins + Accomplishments

Thank You. Lord!

TODAY'S DATE: ______________________

Wake. Pray. & Write

Lord, I'm Casting These Cares Upon You

Today's Wins + Accomplishments

Thank You, Lord!

TODAY'S DATE: ______________________

Wake, Pray, & Write

Lord, I'm Casting These Cares Upon You

Today's Wins + Accomplishments

Thank You, Lord!

TODAY'S DATE: ______________________

Wake. Pray. & Write

Lord, I'm Casting These Cares Upon You

Today's Wins + Accomplishments

Thank You, Lord!

TODAY'S DATE: ______________________

Wake. Pray. & Write

Lord, I'm Casting These Cares Upon You

Today's Wins + Accomplishments

Thank You, Lord!

TODAY'S DATE: ______________________

Wake. Pray. & Write

Lord. I'm Casting These Cares Upon You

Today's Wins + Accomplishments

Thank You. Lord!

TODAY'S DATE: ____________________

Wake. Pray. & Write

Lord. I'm Casting These Cares Upon You

Today's Wins + Accomplishments

Thank You. Lord!

TODAY'S DATE: ______________________

Wake. Pray. & Write

Lord, I'm Casting These Cares Upon You

Today's Wins + Accomplishments

Thank You, Lord!

TODAY'S DATE: ____________________

Wake. Pray. & Write

Lord, I'm Casting These Cares Upon You

Today's Wins + Accomplishments

Thank You, Lord!

TODAY'S DATE: ______________________

Wake. Pray. & Write

Lord, I'm Casting These Cares Upon You

Today's Wins + Accomplishments

Thank You, Lord!

TODAY'S DATE: ______________________

Wake, Pray, & Write

Lord, I'm Casting These Cares Upon You

Today's Wins + Accomplishments

Thank You, Lord!

TODAY'S DATE:

Wake, Pray, & Write

Lord, I'm Casting These Cares Upon You

Today's Wins + Accomplishments

Thank You, Lord!

TODAY'S DATE: ______________________

Wake, Pray, & Write

Lord, I'm Casting These Cares Upon You

Today's Wins + Accomplishments

Thank You, Lord!

TODAY'S DATE: ____________________

Wake. Pray. & Write

Lord, I'm Casting These Cares Upon You

Today's Wins + Accomplishments

Thank You, Lord!

TODAY'S DATE: ____________________

Wake, Pray, & Write

Lord, I'm Casting These Cares Upon You

Today's Wins + Accomplishments

Thank You, Lord!

TODAY'S DATE: ______________________

Wake. Pray. & Write

Lord, I'm Casting These Cares Upon You

Today's Wins + Accomplishments

Thank You, Lord!

TODAY'S DATE: ____________________

Wake. Pray. & Write

Lord. I'm Casting These Cares Upon You

Today's Wins + Accomplishments

Thank You. Lord!

TODAY'S DATE: ______________________

Wake. Pray. & Write

Lord, I'm Casting These Cares Upon You

Today's Wins + Accomplishments

Thank You, Lord!

TODAY'S DATE: ______________________

Wake. Pray. & Write

Lord. I'm Casting These Cares Upon You

Today's Wins + Accomplishments

Thank You. Lord!

TODAY'S DATE: ________________

Wake. Pray. & Write

Lord, I'm Casting These Cares Upon You

Today's Wins + Accomplishments

Thank You, Lord!

TODAY'S DATE: ______________________

Wake, Pray, & Write

Lord, I'm Casting These Cares Upon You

Today's Wins + Accomplishments

Thank You, Lord!

TODAY'S DATE: ____________________

Wake. Pray. & Write

Lord, I'm Casting These Cares Upon You

Today's Wins + Accomplishments

Thank You, Lord!

TODAY'S DATE: ____________________

Wake. Pray. & Write

Lord. I'm Casting These Cares Upon You

Today's Wins + Accomplishments

Thank You. Lord!

TODAY'S DATE: ______

Wake. Pray. & Write

Lord, I'm Casting These Cares Upon You

Today's Wins + Accomplishments

Thank You, Lord!

TODAY'S DATE: ______________________

Wake. Pray. & Write

Lord. I'm Casting These Cares Upon You

Today's Wins + Accomplishments

Thank You. Lord!

TODAY'S DATE: ______________________________

Wake, Pray, & Write

Lord, I'm Casting These Cares Upon You

Today's Wins + Accomplishments

Thank You, Lord!

TODAY'S DATE: ______

Wake. Pray. & Write

Lord. I'm Casting These Cares Upon You

Today's Wins + Accomplishments

Thank You. Lord!

TODAY'S DATE: ______________________

Wake. Pray. & Write

Lord, I'm Casting These Cares Upon You

Today's Wins + Accomplishments

Thank You, Lord!

TODAY'S DATE: ________________

Wake. Pray. & Write

Lord, I'm Casting These Cares Upon You

Today's Wins + Accomplishments

Thank You, Lord!

TODAY'S DATE: ______________________

Wake, Pray, & Write

Lord, I'm Casting These Cares Upon You

Today's Wins + Accomplishments

Thank You, Lord!

TODAY'S DATE: ______________________

Wake. Pray. & Write

Lord. I'm Casting These Cares Upon You

Today's Wins + Accomplishments

Thank You. Lord!

TODAY'S DATE: ______________________

Wake. Pray. & Write

Lord, I'm Casting These Cares Upon You

Today's Wins + Accomplishments

Thank You, Lord!

TODAY'S DATE: ______________________

Wake. Pray. & Write

Lord. I'm Casting These Cares Upon You

Today's Wins + Accomplishments

Thank You. Lord!

TODAY'S DATE: ______________________

Wake, Pray, & Write

Lord, I'm Casting These Cares Upon You

Today's Wins + Accomplishments

Thank You, Lord!

TODAY'S DATE: ____________________

Wake, Pray, & Write

Lord, I'm Casting These Cares Upon You

Today's Wins + Accomplishments

Thank You, Lord!

TODAY'S DATE: ______________________

Wake. Pray. & Write

Lord, I'm Casting These Cares Upon You

Today's Wins + Accomplishments

Thank You, Lord!

TODAY'S DATE: ____________________

Wake. Pray. & Write

Lord. I'm Casting These Cares Upon You

Today's Wins + Accomplishments

Thank You. Lord!

TODAY'S DATE: ______________________

Wake. Pray. & Write

Lord, I'm Casting These Cares Upon You

Today's Wins + Accomplishments

Thank You, Lord!

TODAY'S DATE: ____________________

Wake. Pray. & Write

Lord. I'm Casting These Cares Upon You

Today's Wins + Accomplishments

Thank You. Lord!

TODAY'S DATE: ____________________

Wake. Pray. & Write

Lord, I'm Casting These Cares Upon You

Today's Wins + Accomplishments

Thank You, Lord!

TODAY'S DATE: ______________________

Wake. Pray. & Write

Lord. I'm Casting These Cares Upon You

Today's Wins + Accomplishments

Thank You. Lord!

TODAY'S DATE: ______________________

Wake. Pray. & Write

Lord, I'm Casting These Cares Upon You

Today's Wins + Accomplishments

Thank You, Lord!

TODAY'S DATE: ______________________

Wake. Pray. & Write

Lord, I'm Casting These Cares Upon You

Today's Wins + Accomplishments

Thank You, Lord!

TODAY'S DATE: ______________________

Wake. Pray. & Write

Lord, I'm Casting These Cares Upon You

Today's Wins + Accomplishments

Thank You, Lord!

TODAY'S DATE: ______________________________

Wake. Pray. & Write

Lord, I'm Casting These Cares Upon You

Today's Wins + Accomplishments

Thank You, Lord!

TODAY'S DATE: ______________________

Wake. Pray. & Write

Lord, I'm Casting These Cares Upon You

Today's Wins + Accomplishments

Thank You, Lord!

TODAY'S DATE: ______________________

Wake, Pray, & Write

Lord, I'm Casting These Cares Upon You

Today's Wins + Accomplishments

Thank You, Lord!

TODAY'S DATE: ____________________

Wake, Pray, & Write

Lord, I'm Casting These Cares Upon You

Today's Wins + Accomplishments

Thank You, Lord!

TODAY'S DATE: ____________________

Wake, Pray, & Write

Lord, I'm Casting These Cares Upon You

Today's Wins + Accomplishments

Thank You, Lord!

TODAY'S DATE: ______________________________

Wake, Pray, & Write

Lord, I'm Casting These Cares Upon You

Today's Wins + Accomplishments

Thank You, Lord!

TODAY'S DATE: ______________________

Wake, Pray, & Write

Lord, I'm Casting These Cares Upon You

Today's Wins + Accomplishments

Thank You, Lord!

TODAY'S DATE: ______________________

Wake, Pray, & Write

Lord, I'm Casting These Cares Upon You

Today's Wins + Accomplishments

Thank You, Lord!

TODAY'S DATE:

Wake, Pray, & Write

Lord, I'm Casting These Cares Upon You

Today's Wins + Accomplishments

Thank You, Lord!

TODAY'S DATE: ________________

Wake. Pray. & Write

Lord. I'm Casting These Cares Upon You

Today's Wins + Accomplishments

Thank You. Lord!

TODAY'S DATE: ______________________

Wake. Pray. & Write

Lord. I'm Casting These Cares Upon You

Today's Wins + Accomplishments

Thank You. Lord!

TODAY'S DATE: ______________________

Wake. Pray. & Write

Lord, I'm Casting These Cares Upon You

Today's Wins + Accomplishments

Thank You, Lord!

TODAY'S DATE: ____________________

Wake, Pray, & Write

Lord, I'm Casting These Cares Upon You

Today's Wins + Accomplishments

Thank You, Lord!

TODAY'S DATE: ______________________

Wake. Pray. & Write

Lord, I'm Casting These Cares Upon You

Today's Wins + Accomplishments

Thank You, Lord!

TODAY'S DATE: ____________________

Wake. Pray. & Write

Lord, I'm Casting These Cares Upon You

Today's Wins + Accomplishments

Thank You, Lord!

TODAY'S DATE: ______________________

Wake. Pray. & Write

Lord, I'm Casting These Cares Upon You

Today's Wins + Accomplishments

Thank You, Lord!

TODAY'S DATE: ______________________

Wake, Pray, & Write

Lord, I'm Casting These Cares Upon You

Today's Wins + Accomplishments

Thank You, Lord!

TODAY'S DATE: ____________

Wake. Pray. & Write

Lord. I'm Casting These Cares Upon You

Today's Wins + Accomplishments

Thank You. Lord!

TODAY'S DATE: ______________________

Wake. Pray. & Write

Lord. I'm Casting These Cares Upon You

Today's Wins + Accomplishments

Thank You. Lord!

TODAY'S DATE: ______________________

Wake, Pray, & Write

Lord, I'm Casting These Cares Upon You

Today's Wins + Accomplishments

Thank You, Lord!

TODAY'S DATE: ____________________

Wake. Pray. & Write

Lord. I'm Casting These Cares Upon You

Today's Wins + Accomplishments

Thank You. Lord!

TODAY'S DATE: ______________________

Wake. Pray. & Write

Lord, I'm Casting These Cares Upon You

Today's Wins + Accomplishments

Thank You, Lord!

TODAY'S DATE: ______________________

Wake. Pray. & Write

Lord. I'm Casting These Cares Upon You

Today's Wins + Accomplishments

Thank You. Lord!

TODAY'S DATE: ______________________

Wake. Pray. & Write

Lord, I'm Casting These Cares Upon You

Today's Wins + Accomplishments

Thank You, Lord!

TODAY'S DATE: ______________________

Wake. Pray. & Write

Lord. I'm Casting These Cares Upon You

Today's Wins + Accomplishments

Thank You. Lord!

TODAY'S DATE: ______________________

Wake, Pray, & Write

Lord, I'm Casting These Cares Upon You

Today's Wins + Accomplishments

Thank You, Lord!

TODAY'S DATE: ______________________

Wake, Pray, & Write

Lord, I'm Casting These Cares Upon You

Today's Wins + Accomplishments

Thank You, Lord!

TODAY'S DATE: ______________________

Wake. Pray. & Write

Lord. I'm Casting These Cares Upon You

Today's Wins + Accomplishments

Thank You. Lord!

TODAY'S DATE: ______________________

Wake, Pray, & Write

Lord, I'm Casting These Cares Upon You

Today's Wins + Accomplishments

Thank You, Lord!

TODAY'S DATE: ____________________

Wake. Pray. & Write

Lord, I'm Casting These Cares Upon You

Today's Wins + Accomplishments

Thank You, Lord!

TODAY'S DATE: ______________________

Wake. Pray. & Write

Lord. I'm Casting These Cares Upon You

Today's Wins + Accomplishments

Thank You. Lord!

TODAY'S DATE: ________________

Wake, Pray, & Write

Lord, I'm Casting These Cares Upon You

Today's Wins + Accomplishments

Thank You, Lord!

TODAY'S DATE:

Wake, Pray, & Write

Lord, I'm Casting These Cares Upon You

Today's Wins + Accomplishments

Thank You, Lord!

TODAY'S DATE: ______________________

Wake, Pray, & Write

Lord, I'm Casting These Cares Upon You

Today's Wins + Accomplishments

Thank You, Lord!

TODAY'S DATE: ______________________

Wake. Pray. & Write

Lord. I'm Casting These Cares Upon You

Today's Wins + Accomplishments

Thank You. Lord!

TODAY'S DATE: ______________________

Wake, Pray, & Write

Lord, I'm Casting These Cares Upon You

Today's Wins + Accomplishments

Thank You, Lord!

TODAY'S DATE: ____________________

Wake. Pray. & Write

Lord. I'm Casting These Cares Upon You

Today's Wins + Accomplishments

Thank You. Lord!

TODAY'S DATE: ______________________________

Wake, Pray, & Write

Lord, I'm Casting These Cares Upon You

Today's Wins + Accomplishments

Thank You, Lord!

TODAY'S DATE: ______________________

Wake. Pray. & Write

Lord. I'm Casting These Cares Upon You

Today's Wins + Accomplishments

Thank You. Lord!

TODAY'S DATE: ______________________

Wake. Pray. & Write

Lord, I'm Casting These Cares Upon You

Today's Wins + Accomplishments

Thank You, Lord!

TODAY'S DATE: ______________________

Wake. Pray. & Write

Lord. I'm Casting These Cares Upon You

Today's Wins + Accomplishments

Thank You. Lord!

TODAY'S DATE: ____________________

Wake. Pray. & Write

Lord. I'm Casting These Cares Upon You

Today's Wins + Accomplishments

Thank You. Lord!

TODAY'S DATE: ____________________

Wake. Pray. & Write

Lord. I'm Casting These Cares Upon You

Today's Wins + Accomplishments

Thank You. Lord!

TODAY'S DATE: ____________________

Wake. Pray. & Write

Lord, I'm Casting These Cares Upon You

Today's Wins + Accomplishments

Thank You, Lord!

TODAY'S DATE: ____________________

Wake. Pray. & Write

Lord. I'm Casting These Cares Upon You

Today's Wins + Accomplishments

Thank You. Lord!

TODAY'S DATE: ____________________

Wake. Pray. & Write

Lord, I'm Casting These Cares Upon You

Today's Wins + Accomplishments

Thank You, Lord!

TODAY'S DATE: ______________________

Wake. Pray. & Write

Lord, I'm Casting These Cares Upon You

Today's Wins + Accomplishments

Thank You, Lord!

TODAY'S DATE: ______________________

Wake. Pray. & Write

Lord. I'm Casting These Cares Upon You

Today's Wins + Accomplishments

Thank You. Lord!

TODAY'S DATE: ______________________

Wake. Pray. & Write

Lord, I'm Casting These Cares Upon You

Today's Wins + Accomplishments

Thank You, Lord!

TODAY'S DATE: ______________________

Wake. Pray. & Write

Lord, I'm Casting These Cares Upon You

Today's Wins + Accomplishments

Thank You, Lord!

TODAY'S DATE: ______________________

Wake, Pray, & Write

Lord, I'm Casting These Cares Upon You

Today's Wins + Accomplishments

Thank You, Lord!

TODAY'S DATE: ____________________

Wake. Pray. & Write

Lord, I'm Casting These Cares Upon You

Today's Wins + Accomplishments

Thank You, Lord!

TODAY'S DATE: ______________________

Wake. Pray. & Write

Lord. I'm Casting These Cares Upon You

Today's Wins + Accomplishments

Thank You. Lord!

TODAY'S DATE: ______________________

Wake. Pray. & Write

Lord. I'm Casting These Cares Upon You

Today's Wins + Accomplishments

Thank You. Lord!

TODAY'S DATE: ______________________

Wake. Pray. & Write

Lord, I'm Casting These Cares Upon You

Today's Wins + Accomplishments

Thank You, Lord!

TODAY'S DATE: ______________________

Wake, Pray, & Write

Lord, I'm Casting These Cares Upon You

Today's Wins + Accomplishments

Thank You, Lord!

TODAY'S DATE: ______________________

Wake. Pray. & Write

Lord. I'm Casting These Cares Upon You

Today's Wins + Accomplishments

Thank You. Lord!

TODAY'S DATE: ______________________

Wake, Pray, & Write

Lord, I'm Casting These Cares Upon You

Today's Wins + Accomplishments

Thank You, Lord!

TODAY'S DATE: ____________________

Wake, Pray, & Write

Lord, I'm Casting These Cares Upon You

Today's Wins + Accomplishments

Thank You, Lord!

TODAY'S DATE:

Wake. Pray. & Write

Lord. I'm Casting These Cares Upon You

Today's Wins + Accomplishments

Thank You. Lord!

TODAY'S DATE: ______________________

Wake, Pray, & Write

Lord, I'm Casting These Cares Upon You

Today's Wins + Accomplishments

Thank You, Lord!

TODAY'S DATE: ______________________

Wake. Pray. & Write

Lord, I'm Casting These Cares Upon You

Today's Wins + Accomplishments

Thank You, Lord!

TODAY'S DATE:

Wake, Pray, & Write

Lord, I'm Casting These Cares Upon You

Today's Wins + Accomplishments

Thank You, Lord!

TODAY'S DATE: ____________________

Wake. Pray. & Write

Lord. I'm Casting These Cares Upon You

Today's Wins + Accomplishments

Thank You. Lord!

TODAY'S DATE: ______________________

Wake. Pray. & Write

Lord. I'm Casting These Cares Upon You

Today's Wins + Accomplishments

Thank You. Lord!

TODAY'S DATE: ______________________

Wake. Pray. & Write

Lord, I'm Casting These Cares Upon You

Today's Wins + Accomplishments

Thank You, Lord!

TODAY'S DATE: ______________________

Wake. Pray. & Write

Lord, I'm Casting These Cares Upon You

Today's Wins + Accomplishments

Thank You, Lord!

TODAY'S DATE: ____________________

Wake. Pray. & Write

Lord, I'm Casting These Cares Upon You

Today's Wins + Accomplishments

Thank You, Lord!

TODAY'S DATE: ______________________

Wake, Pray, & Write

Lord, I'm Casting These Cares Upon You

Today's Wins + Accomplishments

Thank You, Lord!

TODAY'S DATE: ______________________________

Wake. Pray. & Write

Lord, I'm Casting These Cares Upon You

Today's Wins + Accomplishments

Thank You, Lord!

TODAY'S DATE: ______________________________

Wake. Pray. & Write

Lord. I'm Casting These Cares Upon You

Today's Wins + Accomplishments

Thank You. Lord!

TODAY'S DATE:

Wake, Pray, & Write

Lord, I'm Casting These Cares Upon You

Today's Wins + Accomplishments

Thank You, Lord!

TODAY'S DATE: ____________________

Wake, Pray, & Write

Lord, I'm Casting These Cares Upon You

Today's Wins + Accomplishments

Thank You, Lord!

TODAY'S DATE: ____________________

Wake, Pray, & Write

Lord, I'm Casting These Cares Upon You

Today's Wins + Accomplishments

Thank You, Lord!

TODAY'S DATE: ______________________

Wake, Pray, & Write

Lord, I'm Casting These Cares Upon You

Today's Wins + Accomplishments

Thank You, Lord!

TODAY'S DATE: ______________________

Wake. Pray. & Write

Lord, I'm Casting These Cares Upon You

Today's Wins + Accomplishments

Thank You, Lord!

TODAY'S DATE: ______________________

Wake. Pray. & Write

Lord. I'm Casting These Cares Upon You

Today's Wins + Accomplishments

Thank You. Lord!

TODAY'S DATE: ______________________

Wake, Pray, & Write

Lord, I'm Casting These Cares Upon You

Today's Wins + Accomplishments

Thank You, Lord!

TODAY'S DATE: ______________________

Wake, Pray, & Write

Lord, I'm Casting These Cares Upon You

Today's Wins + Accomplishments

Thank You, Lord!

TODAY'S DATE: ______________________

Wake. Pray. & Write

Lord, I'm Casting These Cares Upon You

Today's Wins + Accomplishments

Thank You, Lord!

For great is His
love toward us. and the
faithfulness of the
LORD endures forever.
Praise the LORD.
PSALM 117:2 NIV

Closing Reflections

Dear Sis,

Praise the Lord! Truly, He has done awesome and mighty works in your life. I pray that your relationship with God has blossomed and your faith and trust in Him has been elevated. Certainly, when you look back over your life, specifically the past 365 days, you can say that God is faithful and His Favor has indeed rested upon you.

As you have written in this journal, or, as you may be reading this page before you've begun writing, please take a moment now to **share a review on *www.Amazon.com*** including a description of how this journal *has* or *will* greatly complement your walk with God. Your review on *Amazon.com* is greatly appreciated!

Additionally, let's connect on social media! I'd love to "see" and meet you, plus know what God is doing in your life!

LET'S CONNECT

Follow on Facebook: @TeresaReneeHunt
Follow on Instagram: @TeresaReneeHunt
Subscribe on Youtube: @TeresaReneeHunt
Subscribe to the Podcast: *www.teresareneehunt.com/podcast*

COMPLIMENTARY GIFT

Your words have the power to shape your world.

Change Your Words, Change Your Life: Powerful Declarations for the Purpose-Driven Woman is a **free *e-guide*** which includes ten Bible-based declarations and scriptures that will fortify your faith and empower you to walk boldly in your purpose.

Download your free copy: ***www.teresareneehunt.com/declarations***

About the Author

Teresa Renee Hunt is an ordained minister, educator, and the founder of Truth2RenewHearts Enterprises LLC, a life-enrichment brand that equips women and leaders for spiritual growth and personal success.

As visionary and lead writing consultant of Truth2RenewHearts Publishing Consultancy, Teresa also teaches professional and ministry leaders how to package their expertise and experience into a powerful publication so they can expand their influence and magnify their Kingdom message. Teresa has been recognized as one of Pittsburgh's FAB40 by the New Pittsburgh Courier and she is the author of *Positioned to Be Found: How to Prepare Yourself for Marriage Right Now.*

Teresa Renee is married to Dr. Julian E. Hunt and she is the proud mother of two. She holds degrees in Education and School Administration from Edinboro University of Pennsylvania, and a Christian Leadership Certification from Geneva College Center for Urban Biblical Ministries. Upon completion, she will have a second Master's degree in Pastoral Counseling with an emphasis in Marriage & Family Counseling.

From one-on-one coaching, virtual classes, books, and her online ministry, women are empowered to walk in their purpose, and challenged to live authentically & powerfully while glorifying God in all facets of their lives. To learn more, or to book Teresa to speak, you can visit *www.teresareneehunt.com.*

Made in the USA
Monee, IL
29 May 2022